25 POP TUNES FOR PIANO GRADED

in Dip

CW00350029

Published by
Wise Publications
14-15 Berners Street, London W1T 3LJ, UK.

Exclusive Distributors:
Music Sales Limited
Distribution Centre, Newmarket Road,
Bury St Edmunds, Suffolk IP33 3YB, UK.
Music Sales Corporation
180 Madison Avenue, 24th Floor, New York NY 10010, USA.
Music Sales Pty Limited
20 Resolution Drive, Caringbah, NSW 2229, Australia.

Order No. AM1005829
ISBN 978-1-78038-831-1
This book © Copyright 2012 Wise Publications,
a division of Music Sales Limited.

Edited by Jenni Norey.
Music processed by Camden Music.
Printed in the EU.

Your Guarantee of Quality
As publishers, we strive to produce every book to
the highest commercial standards.
This book has been carefully designed to minimise awkward
page turns and to make playing from it a real pleasure.
Particular care has been given to specifying acid-free, neutral-sized
paper made from pulps which have not been elemental chlorine bleached.
This pulp is from farmed sustainable forests and
was produced with special regard for the environment.
Throughout, the printing and binding have been planned to ensure
a sturdy, attractive publication which should give years of enjoyment.
If your copy fails to meet our high standards,
please inform us and we will gladly replace it.

www.musicsales.com

WISE PUBLICATIONS
part of The Music Sales Group

London / New York / Paris / Sydney / Copenhagen / Berlin / Madrid / Tokyo

GRADING NOTES

The pieces in this book have been carefully graded according to
various criteria such as rhythmic complexity, phrasing, tempo, key, range, etc.
Look for the number of stars for each piece to give you
an idea of the approximate playing level.
All musicians have particular strengths and weaknesses,
so the grading offered here should be taken as a suggestion only.

Generally, pieces with one star will have simple rhythms
in both hands and straight-forward phrasings.
They are essentially diatonic and in easier keys.

Pieces with two stars will have more challenging passages,
perhaps containing more rhythmic complexity
and possibly exploring a wider range on the keyboard.

Three-star pieces may be in more challenging
keys and include some modulation.
Read through rhythms and keys carefully before playing,
and check for time-signature changes.

A Case Of You
(Joni Mitchell)

Words & Music by Joni Mitchell

With feeling ♩ = 100

Fine

D.S. al Fine

The A Team
(Ed Sheeran)

Words & Music by Ed Sheeran

Moderately ♩ = 86

Fireflies
(Owl City)

Words & Music by Adam Young

Con pedale

mp (f)

to Coda

1.

2.

Greatest Day
(Take That)

Words & Music by Mark Owen, Gary Barlow, Jason Orange & Howard Donald

Moving forward ♩ = 110

Have A Nice Day
(Stereophonics)

Words & Music by Kelly Jones

Medium rock ♩ = 120

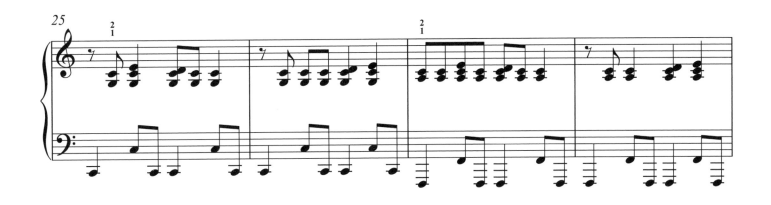

to Coda ⊕

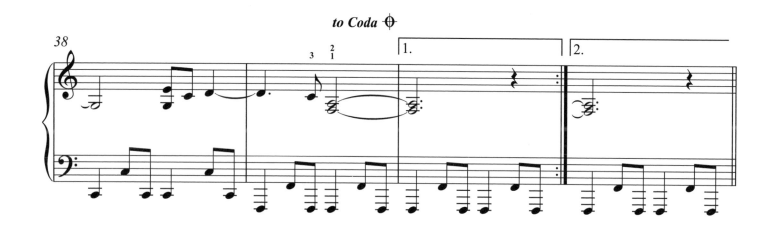

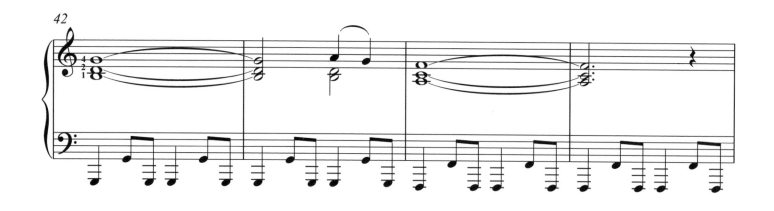

D.S. al Coda

⊕ Coda

Repeat to fade

Halo
(Beyoncé)

Words & Music by Ryan Tedder, Beyoncé Knowles & Evan Bogart

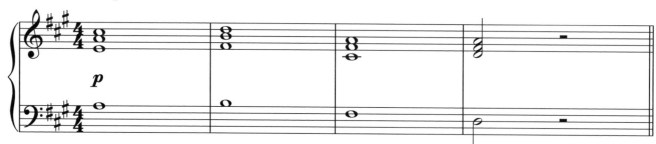

Con pedale

D.S. al Coda

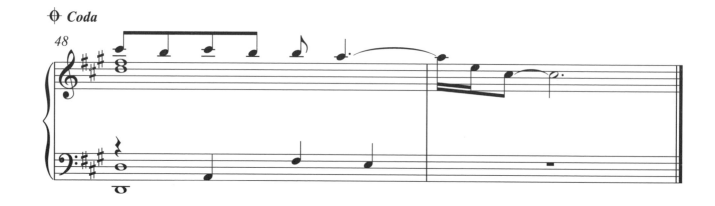

Hide And Seek
(Imogen Heap)

Words & Music by Imogen Heap

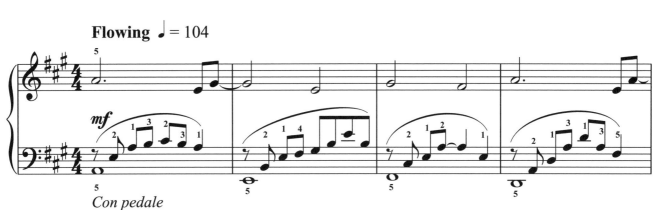

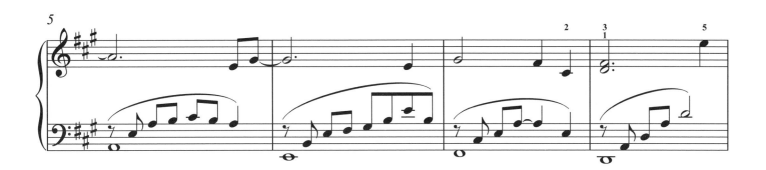

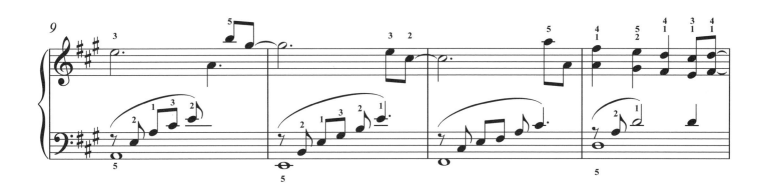

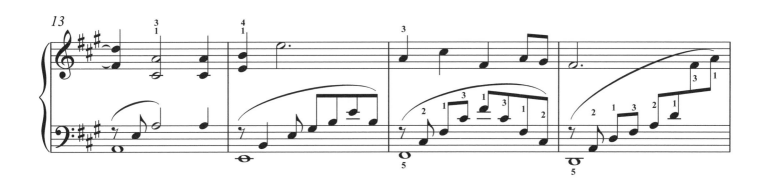

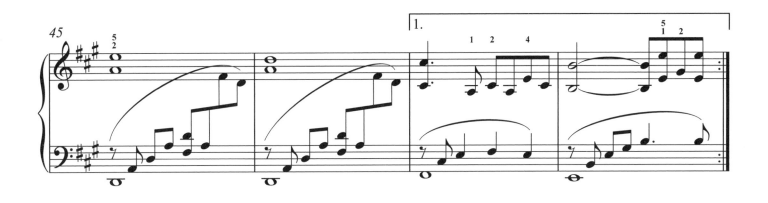

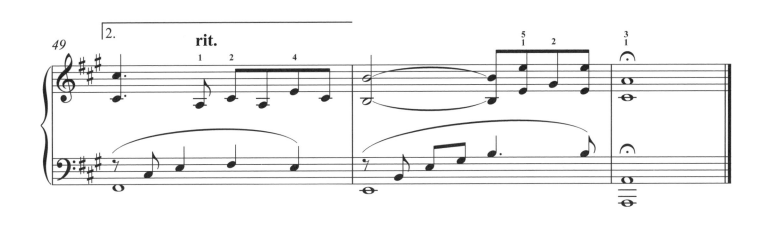

Homeward Bound
(Simon And Garfunkel)

Words & Music by Paul Simon

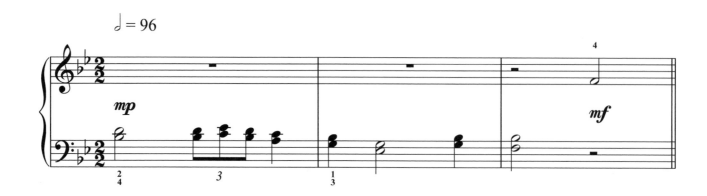

Con pedale

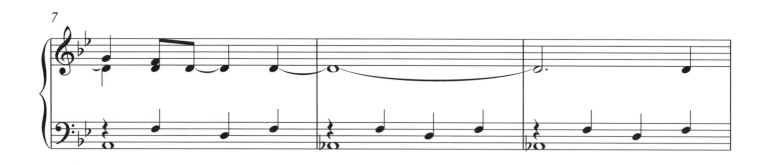

I Won't Let You Go
(James Morrison)

Words & Music by Martin Brammer, Steve Robson & James Morrison

Moderate ballad tempo

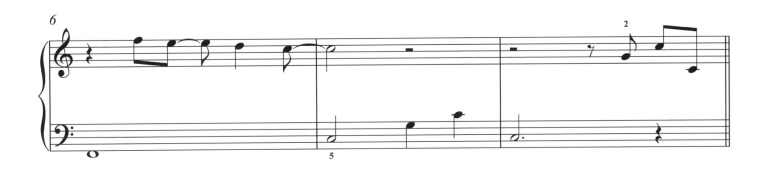

34

D.S. al Fine

Just The Way You Are
(Bruno Mars)

Words & Music by Ari Levine, Bruno Mars, Philip Lawrence, Peter Hernandez, Khari Cain & Khalil Walton

Like A Rolling Stone
(Bob Dylan)

Words & Music by Bob Dylan

Love Goes Down
(Plan B)

Words & Music by Benjamin Drew, Eric Appapoulay, Richard Cassell & Tom Goss

♩ = 100

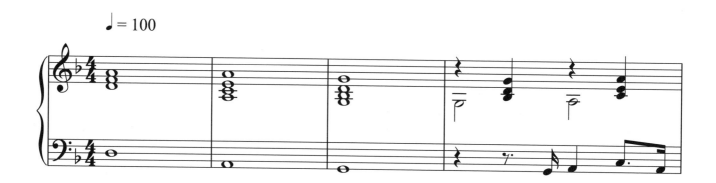

Love Story
(Taylor Swift)

Words & Music by Taylor Swift

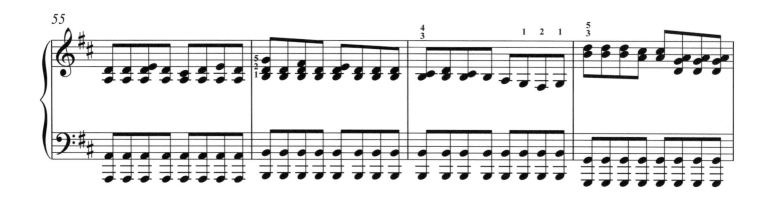

D.S. al Coda

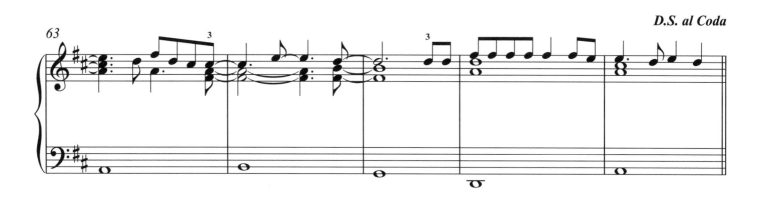

Coda

Paradise
(Coldplay)

Words & Music by Chris Martin, Guy Berryman, Jon Buckland, Will Champion & Brian Eno

D.S. al Fine

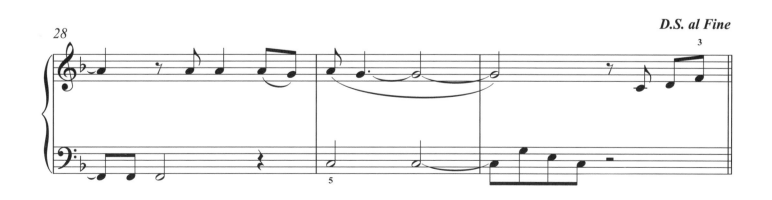

Poker Face
(Lady Gaga)

Words & Music by Stefani Germanotta & Nadir Khayat

Moderato ♩ = 120

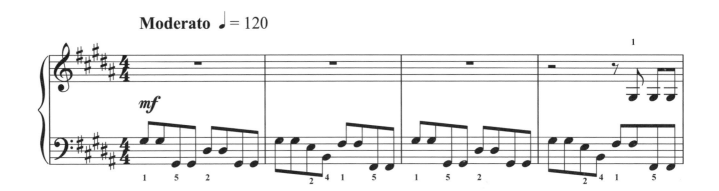

Price Tag
(Jessie J)

Words & Music by Lukasz Gottwald, Claude Kelly, Bobby Ray Simmons & Jessica Cornish

Run
(Snow Patrol)

Words & Music by Gary Lightbody, Jonathan Quinn, Mark McClelland, Nathan Connolly & Iain Archer

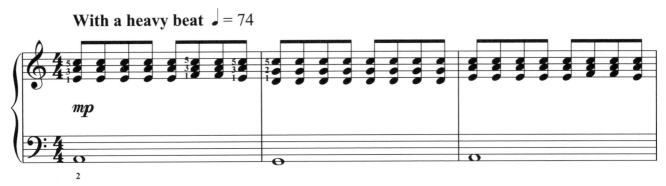

D.S. al Coda

Coda

Rolling In The Deep
(Adele)

Words & Music by Adele Adkins & Paul Epworth

With a driving beat ♩ = 104

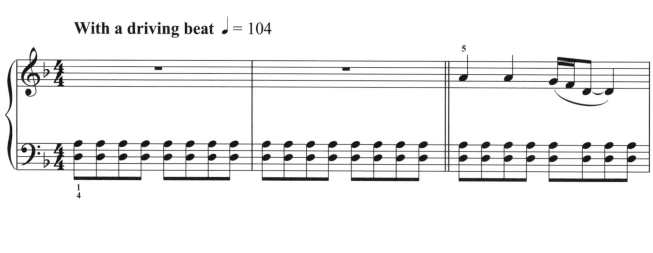

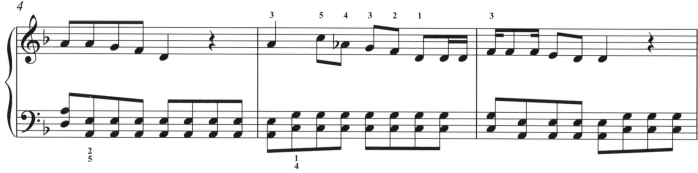

She Loves You
(The Beatles)

Words & Music by John Lennon & Paul McCartney

Moderately bright

Slow
(Rumer)

Words & Music by Sarah Joyce

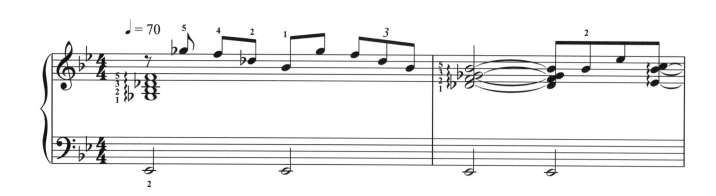

78

Somewhere Only We Know
(Keane)

Words & Music by Tim Rice-Oxley, Tom Chaplin & Richard Hughes

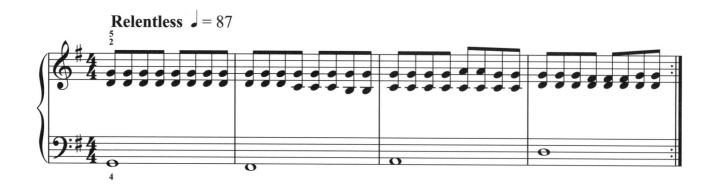

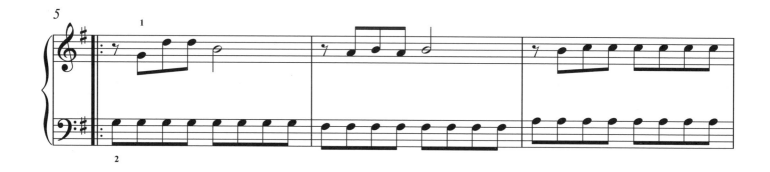

The Tide Is High
(Blondie)

Words & Music by John Holt, Bill Padley, Howard Barrett, Jem Godfrey & Tyrone Evans

Repeat to fade

Waterloo
(ABBA)

Words & Music by Benny Andersson, Stig Anderson & Björn Ulvaeus

Bright shuffle

Your Song
(Elton John)

Words & Music by Elton John & Bernie Taupin

What Makes You Beautiful
(One Direction)

Words & Music by Savan Kotecha, Carl Falk & Rami Yacoub

123456789